Forward

Forward

This project was built upon the business planning initiatives of the Canadian Farm Business Management Council's Rural Business Planner CD. There was an identified need within the farm community for a booklet version of a rural business planner guide similar to the popular Rural Business Planner CD. The objectives in creating this publication were to stimulate business planning by more farm/ranch businesses, to simplify the business planning process wherever possible and to illustrate the value of business planning as an important business

management tool. Plain and simple, business planning is a management tool that can be used to reduce risk and increase your chances of success. Successful businesses are built over time as a result of thoughtful planning and the resulting actions. It is hard to imagine that anyone setting off on a journey that was to extend over many years, such as running a farm/ ranch business, would not have a well thought out plan. Starting, running and succeeding in your business will be enhanced through business planning initiatives. The author's hope is that readers will use the stepping stones found in this book to guide them on the path to creating a business plan and move their farm/ranch enterprises to new levels of business sustainability and success.

Good planning, new success and fair returns!

Authors: R. Gary Morton and Bev Connell

Acknowledgements

Acknowledgements

Authors:

R. Gary Morton, Morton Horticultural Associates

Bev Connell, ProAgri Consulting Limited

Contributors:

Content Advisors and Editors: Don Singer

Project Manager: Don Singer, Ottawa, Ontario

Publisher and Distributor:

Canadian Farm Business Management Council

300-250 City Centre

Ottawa, Ontario, K1R 6K7

Phone:1-888-232-3262 **Fax:**1-800-270-8301

Email: council@cfbmc.com   **Web:** www.farmcentre.com

Designer: Little Horse Communications

Printer: Cielo Print Inc.

Contributing Partners:

Produced by CFBMC through funding from the Agriculture Policy
Framework Renewal Programs of Agriculture and Agri-Food Canada.

ISBN 1-894148-95-9

CFBMC

CFBMC

Canadian Farm Business Management Council

The Canadian Farm Business Management Council (CFBMC) is the only national organization in Canada devoted exclusively to developing and distributing advanced farm management information.

CFBMC is supported by Agriculture and Agri-Food Canada and a growing number of industry partners. CFBMC's wide range of information products and services such as publications, CD-ROM's, videos, conferences, bi-monthly newsletter and web-site cover topics of relevance to farmers such as science and innovation, business risk management, farm transfer and succession planning, marketing, financial and human resources management and farm diversification. These products and services, produced in collaboration with industry, the educational sector as well as the provinces and territories, help to address the management information needs of Canadian farmers in a globally competitive environment.

Disclaimer

Agriculture and Agri-Food Canada is pleased to participate in the production of this publication and is committed to working with our industry partners to increase public awareness of the importance of the agri-food industry to Canada. Opinions expressed in this document are those of the authors and do not necessary reflect those of the Department or the Government of Canada.

The text and precedents contained in this publication are offered as an aid to professional competence with the understanding that the contributors are not providing specific legal or consulting advice. The reader must exercise judgment about the applicability of the information contained herein, and obtain professional advice where applicable. The Canadian Farm Business Management Council and the contributors do not take responsibility for the outcome of any actions taken as a result of applying any material contained herein.

The table of contents

The table of contents

1.0 All about business planning

"If your idea doesn't work on paper, then it won't work in real life, and you'll have just saved yourself a whole lot of time and money".

Alan Streatch, C.E.O. Granview Farms Ltd., Elderbank, Nova Scotia

1.1 An introduction to business planning

A farm business is successful for many different reasons.

A common characteristic of successful farm/ranch enterprises is that they devote time and energy to business planning. They consciously have an up to date plan, and then integrate that plan into their daily business activities and operations. These producers have recognized that business planning contributes to the creation of a sustainable future for their farm or ranch. Business planning saves them time, money, reduces their risk and improves the communication within their family, with their staff and with other important stakeholders.

Many farmers/ranchers do have a business plan; but unfortunately it's locked away in their head and is rarely shared with their family or staff. Others hire out the preparation of their business plan, using it to obtain financing for a specific project and then they banish the plan to some hidden filing cabinet to collect dust. However, more and more farm entrepreneurs are realizing the value in using their business plan as a powerful business management tool. They see a business plan as a document that outlines a picture of a desired farm/ranch future that can easily be shared, articulated and communicated with the team of stakeholders that can help turn their vision into a future reality.

By nature most farmers/ranchers are action oriented, preferring to get out on the land and "just do it", rather than to sit in an office "planning" and "wasting precious time". It is exactly for this reason that many producers still jump into a new business venture with reckless abandon and little more than hope in a hand basket. It's the o'l entrepreneurial fly by the seat of your pants confidence; shoot from the hip and come in with both guns a blaz'n, and eventually things will work themselves out. It would be great if that really were the case, but in today's extremely competitive marketplace, there is little room for any rash business decisions that have not been well "thought out" and "planned". Globalization has created a queue (lineup) of aggressive producers from around the world, waiting for the North American farmer/rancher to make a crucial business mistake so that they can take away his/her market share. Planning and business planning is no longer an option for a farm/ranch business. It is the most important and critical risk management tool in a modern farm/ranch manager's business management tool box.

1.1.1 What is a "farm" business plan?

What is a "farm" business plan?

At one time a "rural" or "farm" business was significantly different from an urban based business. Rural business was primarily the "production" of raw inputs and urban business was the "manufacturing" and "delivery" to the market of those raw inputs. In reality, farming today is in the interface, the quasi-grey area between urban and rural business. As commodity agriculture margins have declined in recent years, many producers are choosing to evolve and transform their farms/ranches through value adding, diversification and innovation. They are moving up the value chain into manufacturing, further processing and selling direct to the end consumer. The distinct boundaries or differences that may have once existed between urban and rural businesses are quickly disappearing as the two blend together. Many successful farm based businesses are operating deep within this interface zone. Whether you raise cattle or hogs, are in agri-tourism or value added processing, grow floriculture or fruit, produce vegetable or specialty crops, sell at a farm market or are in supply management; a business plan is a blueprint for your farm/ranch business's success and a map to your future.

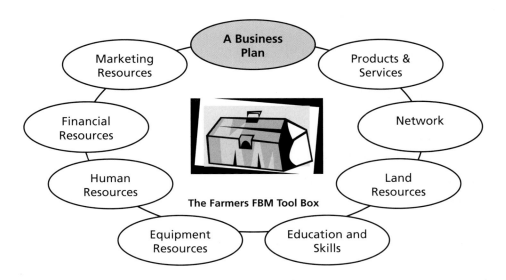

1.1.2 Why do I need a business plan?

Why do I need a business plan?

I have done pretty well so far without a business plan; why do I need one now?

While the question is a fair one to ask, there are a number of reasons why the development of a business plan should be considered an extremely important activity for any farm/ranch business. In simple terms a plan is a means to an ends. A plan focuses your organizations efforts, on your priorities, on the actions that need to be done; it develops timelines and is a very effective communication tool for reducing confusion. Planning ultimately saves you time, reduces the risk of making mistakes, anticipates the future, analyzes market opportunities, explores contingency options, examines feasibility, identifies the required resources and finances, involves stakeholders, creates buy in and in the end helps you facilitate the achievement of your dreams. A business plan helps you get to where it is that you want to go.

You may never have had to prepare a business plan in the past and you may have done OK without one to this point. But keep in mind that the past does not necessarily equal your future. Possibly your business circumstances may have changed in recent years. Has your business become more complex and challenging? Are you carrying more debt and have the market stakes and risks increased? Have you recently been subjected to new regulations? Are your breeds or varieties falling out of favour with the consumer? Do you have a new market opportunity to explore? Does your business have more staff than in the past? Do you want to slow down? Is there a family member waiting in the wings and is it time to start the process of passing the business on to the next generation? For a multitude of reasons, as time passes your circumstances change and so does your business environment. A successful business is a living, dynamic, continually changing enterprise. Typically farmers/ranchers are busy in the daily grind and don't take enough time to examine the big picture and to ensure that their business is moving in the right direction. When you are busy it is easy to let incremental change creep up on you and then before you know it big change has occurred and you must react. Business planning is an excellent way to monitor and benchmark your business environment changes and to act proactively as a farm/ranch business. Each business plan you create is a snap shot, a moment in time, a reference point that can be referred to when evaluating and monitoring your businesses progress and success.

A plan will help you determine if you are going forward or backwards, if new strategies are required and how close and quickly you have moved towards your future vision. Planning will ultimately help you better identify, analyze and evaluate your future business options and help you make better more informed management decisions.

1.1.3 Business growth occurs in phases

Business growth occurs in phases

Business growth normally occurs in phases. Points or plateaus are reached where management decisions and new investments are required in order to reach the next business level. Typically there are four separate phases in a business's life cycle. Phase 1 is a start up phase when your business is getting underway. It requires the development and selling of your idea, obtaining financing, finding customers, setting up your business enterprise and basically keeping the wolf from the door. Phase 2 is a growth phase; your business is gaining market experience, you capitalize on your opportunities and you find your formula for success and profit. This can be a time of good returns but also high costs and rapid change. Phase 3 is a mature phase where your markets are well established, but competition is stiff and your profit margins may start to level off or decline. You begin or should begin looking at ways to reinvent your business or value-add your products and services. Phase 4 is the decline phase that follows the mature business phase. The decline phase is when demand for your product or service starts to decline and margins shrink rapidly. If you have been unsuccessful at reinventing your business, or value adding your products and services you may decide at this point to wind down your business operation. Different decisions of different complexity are required at different stages of your business's life. Business planning is the key management tool that helps you move smoothly between the phases, it allows you to anticipate the inevitable change, growth, and will help you evaluate the information at hand and ultimately help you to make better more informed business decisions. A plan can be your most useful decision tool in helping you determine when to grow, when to change, when it is time to get out or when it is time to transfer the business to someone else with new energy and ideas. Business planning can help you recognize business change and to identify actions that will help your business avoid becoming caught in the decline phase.

Business Life Cycle Phases

	Phase #1 Start Up Phase	Phase #2 Growth Phase	Phase #3 Mature Phase	Phase #4 Decline Phase
Phase Focus	• Survival • Finding Markets • Keeping Markets • Technical Skill • Controlling the Business • Staff Development	• Management Structure • Creating Profit • Maintaining and Managing Growth • Financing Growth • Fending Off Competition • New Expansion Opportunities	• Locate New Markets • Reinvent Existing Products • Explore New Products & Services • Fending Off Competition • Protect Market Share & Position • Succession	• New Injection of Cash • Sell Business • Succession • Exit Strategy
Business Complexity and Need For Business Planning Grows				

1.1.4 Getting to your future

Getting to your future

Everyone has their own unique and noble objectives for being in farming. However, from a business management point of view, you are basically in farming/ranching for three basic reasons.

(1) **To run a successful and profitable farm business.**

(2) **To create long-term security for your retirement.**

(3) **To eventually sell, or pass the business on to someone else.**

These are basic objectives that most farmers and ranchers strive to achieve over their working careers. Typically this involves a time frame of some 30 to 35 years for most farmers and ranchers.

Would you build a barn without a plan? Some might, but municipalities don't allow it because they see it as too risky; the barn could fall down and someone might get hurt. There could be consequences of a poorly planned barn.

Would you tear a tractor apart without a reference shop manual? Some might, but as tractors become more complex the likelihood of getting it back together right without a reference shop manual are limited.

Would you set out on a family vacation without first thoroughly planning where you will go, what you might do and how much it will cost? You might get away without much planning if the vacation was only for a week or so.

But let's say that your family vacation was extended to a trip that would take you, say 30 or 35 years. For most people planning would now not only be important, it would become a critical action. You would need and want to know how much money will be required, where it will come from and when. You'll also want to know where you will lodge, how you will feed your family and what will be the mode of transport from place to place. Potential risks and dangers would be analyzed and you would identify who would be available to help you along your journey. In this situation most would consider a detailed plan a rather important reference tool. Something that they could refer to frequently to monitor and benchmark their progress and ensure that eventually they get to where it is that they wanted to go and then successfully back home. This is no different from you planning the journey of your families farm /ranch business from where you are today to your retirement at some distant point in the future. If you know where you want to be in 30 years then you know where you need to be in 20, 10, 5, 3, 2, and next year. This is real life; and it's your life! Planning helps you and your family ensure that you get to a successful future, in the minimum amount of time with the least amount of problems and risk.

There was a time when the weather was the biggest worry for a farmer. What was produced people bought and you did OK. The competitive marketplace a farm/ranch business faces today has little sympathy or mercy for those that can't keep up or habitually make poor decisions and frequent business mistakes. In a global agricultural economy, low profit margins make it almost impossible in most commodity markets to recover from a poor year or a major business market mistake. Business planning is the path to your future and your farm/ranches best protection and risk management tool. It is not always easy to plan, but whether you plan or you don't plan; you will eventually reach your future. What your future looks like will be determined in large by how well you planned for success and subsequently turn that plan into a reality for your family.

1.1.5 Planning adds horsepower to your business

To spend valuable time planning without realizing added benefits to your farm/ranch business would be pointless.
It has been well proven that business planning can give your business a valuable extra burst of horsepower that can make the difference in a competitive marketplace. The points below are a few of the ways the business planning process can power up your farm/ranch operation:

- Involving your farm/ranch stakeholders (family & staff) builds credibility and buy-in for your business vision.
- A documented plan can be shared with your team of stakeholders that will help you achieve your goals.
- You identify and outline the required resources, finances,

timelines and strategies necessary for you success.

- You can examine how your business is doing from an outside viewpoint.
- Planning forces you to create options and contingencies for when things don't go as you planned.
- A plan is a blueprint for monitoring your success, a measuring instrument of how well you're doing.
- Mistakes on paper are much less costly than mistakes in real life.
- Planning facilitates opportunities for new partnerships, alliances and investments in your business.
- It increases your likelihood of succeeding in a new farm/ranch venture.

Planning is an ongoing and continual process that when regularly undertaken helps ensure that your business is adapting to the change of it's ever evolving business environment. A business plan is literally an ongoing check up that keeps your farm/ranch powered up. Planning initiatives are tremendous opportunities to learn more about your business and to involve your family and staff in the future growth of your operation.

1.2 The interrelationship of the strategic and business plans

Planning helps get the metaphor "think global, act local" into a practical perspective. When you think global you are thinking strategically looking at your business in a context of the big picture. Your concern is about how the business environment will impact and affect the future sustainability and success of your farm or ranch. Acting locally is putting action to your vision through specific strategies that maximize your strengths and opportunities while minimizing your threats and weaknesses. This all filters down to your daily operations through your business plan, where your incremental daily actions facilitate the achievement of your vision, goals, objectives and dreams. While your strategic plan is different from your business plan, they are dependant on one another and linked in many ways.

1.2.1 Strategic planning (the big picture)

The strategic planning process searches for answers to the following fundamental business questions:

- **Who are we, what do we do, and why?**
- **What do we want our business to be and do in the future, and why?**
- **How do we get from where we are today to the future?**

Strategic planning looks at the longer term vision for your business, often in timeframes of 3-5 years. It contains your vision, mission statement as well as the key objectives and goals that will guide you towards the achievement of your desired results. All business actions should answer the question; does this action move us closer to or farther away from our strategic vision? A strategic plan creates parameters and an overall business focus. Strategic planning helps you to forecast future growth, the associated risks and to create a business situation that protects your current investment in your farm/ranch business. It keeps you focused on your prime strategic business objectives and helps you evaluate how new opportunities could fit into your long-term vision. Success builds from success.

Strategic Plan

↓

Business Plan

↓

Marketing Plan

↓

Financial Plan

↓

H.R Plan

↓

Production Plan

1.2.2 The business plan (operational plan)

The business plan on the other hand is shorter in timeframe than a strategic plan and is focused on business activities and daily operations. Ultimately, as you achieve your business plan, you move your business closer to achieving your strategic vision. That is how the two plans are linked.

Each new enterprise venture needs its own business plan. For example a farm/ranch diversification or value added project is a new enterprise within your existing farm business and should be looked at as a separate venture from your core business and will require a separate business plan. A business plan minimizes what you don't know. It gives you greater business flexibility and an opportunity to create contingencies for the inevitable surprises that could blindside you at some point in the future. A business plan normally contains information on marketing, finances, human resources and production. Naturally a business plan evolves as your business does and it will need regular adjustments along the way. Refer to your plan frequently; as you would to a road map on a long journey; it is your guide to your future and is your best decision making advisor.

1.2.3 Its all part of a bigger puzzle

Your "business vision" is the long-term view of where you see your farm/ranch at some distant point in the future. Your "business mission" defines the businesses operational parameters for achieving the vision. It defines what it is you do, how you do it, why you do it and for whom. Your key "business objectives and goals" are areas where action is necessary to achieve your mission. The business plan is a documentation of the strategies you will use to achieve your goals and objectives. Subsequently, if you achieve your business plan, you will achieve your goals and objectives. By achieving your goals and objectives you will be true to your mission, which will move you closer to your farm/ranch business vision.

Strategic Vision
"Where Your Business is Headed"

....helps you achieve your....

Business Mission
"How You Do Business"

....helps you remain true to your....

Key Objectives & Goals
"Required Levels of Achievement & Actions"

....helps you achieve your....

Business Plan
"Road Map for Next Defined Period"

1.2.4 Planning characteristics of top farm managers

Successful top farm business managers have the following planning characteristics. **They**:

- Create a clear strategic vision for the long-term success of their business.
- Use the strategic plan as a guiding document, referring to it frequently to monitor and evaluate the farm/ranch business performance.
- Create annual business plans to support the success of their strategic vision and plan.
- Involve their team (family & staff) early in the planning process to improve communication and create support for the plan.
- Create a new business plan for each new business enterprise or diversification venture initiative.
- Use professional advisors to assist them in gathering and analyzing the information in support of their planning efforts.
- Are thoroughly involved and take ownership of the planning process.

1.3　The business plan structure

The business plan structure

1.3.1　So what exactly is a business plan?

So what exactly is a business plan?

A business plan is a written document outlining your business concept, idea or project.   It contains your key objectives and goals, your action strategies, how you propose to achieve success, the resources that you will require and the evidence supporting your business and market assumptions.

1.3.2　What is the typical timeframe of a business plan?

What is the typical timeframe of a business plan?

A business plan normally will cover a period of twelve months, until your project is finished or to when you anticipate that you will achieve your project objectives. A business plan may be required to make financial projections beyond a one year timeframe. When business planning stretches too far into the future it becomes a strategic plan. In today's rapidly changing business environment a lot can change in the period of one year.

1.3.3 Should my plan have a particular focus or flavour

A business has many options for change, as the following business change option diagram illustrates. A business can

contract, diversify, reinvent itself, add new value or exit the industry. Each of these changes has a unique planning need, focus or characteristic and each will require a business plan that has a slightly different flavour, or slant towards the intended reader. Some plans will require a greater emphasis in specific areas, while other plans may want to deemphasize certain other points.

Business Change Options

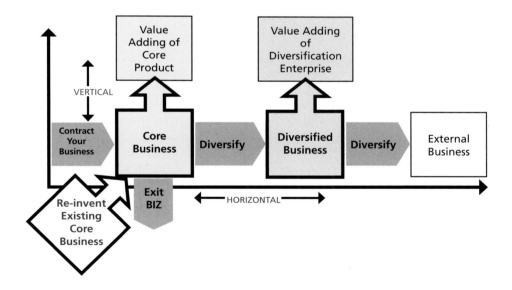

1.3.4 Tailor your plan to the reader

Tailor your plan to the reader

Different business plan readers have differing priorities.
For example a lender is not investing in your business but lending money to your project and is focused on your assets, security, your management skills and your ability to repay the loan. On the other hand investors take ownership in your business and have priorities around their risk in ownership, the profit potential and the eventual recovery of their investment. Other readers will have priorities based on their specific needs and a business plan must be able to address those needs to gain the readers' support.

Reader	What They Are Looking For	What Makes Them Edgy
Banker	- Cash flow, net worth, assets, solid growth.	- Rapid growth, unstable markets, unproven markets, skill deficiencies, limited security.
Investor	- Fast growth, profit potential, recognition of the skills they bring to table, niche market opportunities, proprietary advantages.	- Large markets, commodities.
Large Customer	- Stability, service.	- Fast growth, delivery chain.
Strategic Partners	- Synergy between organizations, proprietary advantages.	- Lack of communication and sharing of information.
Key Staff (Manager)	- Security, development opportunity, business stability.	- Family members, ownership changes, management changes.

1.3.5 Major reasons for a business plan

Major reasons for a business plan

Basically business plans are prepared to develop new ideas, expand or diversify into new markets, start up a new business, reinvent your current business, develop a growing business, add value to what your currently do or plan for a farm transfer/ succession. Some producers religiously prepare an annual business plan to internally monitor their farm/ranch business's progress and growth. These plans will have a very specific focus, usually on performance references such as financial ratios that allow managers to standardize the analysis and comparison of business changes from year to year. Many plans are prepared to raise the capital necessary to finance a major business change. A plan can also be for the purpose of gaining family support or support from a key supplier. Different types of plans require different depths of information and analysis. Some plans are more complicated, while others are very basic and simple. The following table illustrates some common business reasons for preparing a business plan.

Reason	Description	Plans Focus	Complexity of Plan	Focus Towards
Starting a New Business	- Start up business.	- Raising capital - Feasibility of proposal.	- Comprehensive detailed plan.	- Lenders, investors, family, friends.
Seeking Investors	- Need input of new capital for specific project, without increasing debt.	- Raising capital by giving up % of ownership - Feasibility of proposal.	- Comprehensive detailed plan.	- Outside investors, family, friends.
Major Business Change	- Major expansion - Purchase new business. - Diversification - Value Added - Succession	- A change to the core business, may involving refinancing, restructuring, succession planning.	- Comprehensive plan	- Lenders, investors, family, friends
Internal Change	- Management/staff change. - Partial-succession.	- Sharing plans with staff and family.	- Simplified Plan	- Family, staff
Yardstick of Success	- Monitor annual change in business	- Measuring benchmarking annual business performance.	- Simplified plan based on standardized criteria.	- Management team.
Enlist External Support	- Extension of supplier line of credit.	- Obtain support from stakeholder group.	- Readers Digest version, Executive Summary	- Suppliers, customers

1.3.6 The type of business

Your business plan's focus will be determined to a large degree by your specific commodity or the type of business you operate. For example, a business plan created for a typical expansion of a supply managed commodity where lenders are very familiar with the industry, the markets are relatively secure and there is plenty of historical data to support growth, will be significantly different than a business plan created for a new diversification, value added or agri-tourism enterprise where lenders may not have the same knowledge, experience and comfort. A start up business forecasts projections with little or no history to support their assumptions. While an established business has a history and track record to build upon, they may be diversifying into a new area where they also have little experience and history. A start up plan typically will focus on raising capital while a business change plan may focus on gaining staff's support for the change. The table below illustrates examples of different agricultural based businesses and the different slants to their business plans.

Type of Business	Plans Focus	Unique Character of Business	Emphasize In Plan
Typical Commodity (E.g.: Grain, beef, apples, strawberries, broccoli, carrots)	- Increase production of existing known business process. Builds on history and past successes of business.	- Production skills, finances, metrics, common knowledge. - Commodity markets, little differentiation, no unique factors or brands.	- Production skills and efficiencies. - New market opportunities. - Not a major business change.
Supply Managed (E.g.: Dairy, eggs, Poultry)	- Increase production of existing known business process and marketing system. Builds on history and past successes. - Production skills and efficiencies.	- Establish and proven marketing system. - Production skills, finances, metrics common knowledge. - Production efficiency key to success.	- Production skills and efficiencies. - Not a major business change. - Success of supply management.
Specialty Niche (E.g.: Exotics, fish, fur.)	- Develop the opportunity and that your business has the knowledge, market and skills to implement.	- Production skills, finances, metrics not commonly known. - Markets cyclic or new.	- Where you will get your production skills and knowledge. - Markets for new products. - Risk management
Diversification (E.g.: Crop not currently involved in producing.)	- Develop the opportunity and that your business has the resources and skills to implement.	- It is an extension of existing business. - Established track record.- Backup commodity for risk management.	- Production skills and knowledge of new crop. - Financial feasibility and profit potential. - Risk management - HR management.
Value Adding (E.g.: Further processing, new service)	- Develop the opportunity and that your business has the resources and skills to implement. - Processing and market knowledge.	- Production skills, finances, metrics not commonly known.	- Human resources and skills available. - Enhancement of current products. - Risk management strategies.
Agri-tourism (E.g.: Hospitality, accommodations, events, farmers markets)	- Develop the opportunity and that your business has the knowledge, market and skills to implement.	- Production skills, finances, metrics not commonly known. -- Skill and market knowledge.	- Human resources and skills available. - Enhancement of current operation. - Risk management

1.4 Creating the ideal/perfect business plan

Creating the ideal or perfect business plan may seem like a lofty goal, but it is not as hard as it may seem. Business plans normally follow a standard outline or format. A standard format helps readers organize their thoughts and properly evaluate the relevant information. Standardization also reduces the risk of the reader missing any important information. Lenders or investors read many plans over a year and a standardized format save them time and allows for proper comparison of information. The reader wants to know what is involved in your project and what it is that you are asking them for. The measure of an ideal/perfect business plan is in the result; it gets accepted and supported by the intended target reader.

1.4.1 Who should be involved in developing your plan?

There is an old saying; the journey is better than the inn. The business planning process should be seen as an opportunity to learn more about your business, to examine your current management skills and strategies, not just a necessary activity that creates a paper document. The business planning process offers tremendous learning opportunities for all stakeholders. It's a great way to team build with your staff and should be used to create the necessary buy in and support for future change. Identify the stakeholders who could contribute to your planning process. Who will be valuable in helping you achieve our future goals and objectives? Most often you will find your family and staff are the greatest contributors to the planning process. However, you may also want to include trusted professionals such as accountants, lawyers and consultants in the planning process. They bring a valuable outside perspective and should have unbiased opinions and viewpoints. Professional's advisors can be a very useful resource to the development of your farm business plan. They have the advantage of working with and observing many different types of businesses and normally can bring a breadth and depth of experience, information and knowledge to your business planning process. There is often a tendency to abdicate the entire development of your business plan to an independent professional advisor. When a short timeline or deadline is critical, this may be a very good option. However, it is important to still be very involved and manage the planning process. In any case the eventual presenter or pitcher of the business plan must be intimately informed on every aspect of the plan to be seen as credible by the intended audience. This can best be achieved by being totally involved in the planning process.

1.4.2 Write for your reader

No matter who is reading your plan, you can be sure that they are not looking for the comprehensive encyclopedia version on your farm or ranch business. The reader has limited time and is looking for answers to key questions. Your ability to answer those questions and make the answers easy to find will determine if the entire plan is read and your proposal is accepted. Therefore, your objective in writing a business plan should be to tell the complete story in as few words as possible while still supplying all of the necessary supporting information for your business opportunity. Professional lenders and investors review plans on a regular basis and have either experience or corporate policy that they follow when evaluating your business plan. The key points that they are looking for are:

- Your personal background, history and credibility.
- Your net worth and assets available for collateral.
- Your businesses uniqueness in the marketplace.
- Your businesses ability to repay a loan or investment.
- Your businesses ability to make a profit.

The reader in most cases does not have your knowledge on the subject matter.

Don't assume that they do. Make it easy for them to understand. Use diagrams to replace complicated information wherever possible. The reader will be looking for your common sense and proof that your proposed plan is possible. Support assumptions with realistic financials projections and sensitivity analysis. A sensitivity analysis is a range of scenarios', best case, worst case and most likely. It shows you are being realistic in your outlook. Over optimism in your sales and profit projections send up red flags and may lead your reader to question if you are also underestimating your costs and risks. One should also avoid cutting and pasting too much from other plans or sample business plans. While this can save you time, you still need to write a plan that is reflective of your own business. If you borrow heavily from another business plan you risk having a plan that doesn't flow well, has information that you cannot explain and/or creates contradictions.

1.4.3 How long should the plan be?

How long should the plan be?

How long a plan should be is a common question. Typically a plan is 20-30 pages in length when raising money. Remember you only need as many pages as is necessary to tell your story, no more, no less. Respect your reader's time while leaving as few unanswered questions as possible. In all honesty, the longer the document is, the less likely it will get read in its entirety. The business plan is a summary and you can always supply more information upon request or attach/include more information in the appendix. It is a good idea to create a separate appendices document to allow the reader to easily refer to information in the appendices without flipping back and forth. Always try to make it easy for the plans reader.

1.4.4 Writing style

Your writing style needs to be clear and concise. Use short sentences and bullet points wherever possible. Detailed information can be included in the appendix. Be accurate in your analyses and support information with references and footnotes. Use your computer spell checker so that there are no spelling errors or get someone to proof read your plan. Make sure that your plan and especially your financial predictions are believable. A thorough and accurate financial plan illustrates to the reader that you know what you are doing. The plan should look professional, but doesn't need to be fancy or bound; a staple in the corner will suffice.

1.4.5 Where do I get the information to support my plan?

The information that you need to prepare your farm/ranch business plan can be obtained from many sources. Common sources of relevant information are:

- Your company records are a great place to start.
- The Internet and libraries
- Reports, journals & publications
- Industry associations
- Provincial and federal departments of agriculture (Canada and USA)
- Academic institutions (colleges, universities, etc.)
- Other government websites and agencies (Industry Canada, Statistics Canada)
- Consultants, industry advisors and specialists
- Discussions with competitors
- Trade shows
- Surveys of customers and suppliers.

1.4.6 Key sections of a business plan

Key sections of a business plan

Each section of a business plan contains valuable information for the reader. As mentioned before each particular reader looks for specific information and reasons that will allow them to accurately evaluate your business plan. The following are the key sections of a business plan:

- The executive summary is the first and often the only impression your reader may get. The executive summary sells the plan to the reader.
- The business overview establishes credibility with the reader. This is where you proven your "business" is worthy of investment.
- The project opportunity highlights what the plan is focusing on and what it is asking for from the reader.
- The product section describes the product or service that you produce or offer.
- The marketing section proves that you have a market for your product or service and demonstrates that you have the means to gain a suitable market share.
- The operations section shows that you have the resources, knowledge and technical expertise to produce your product or service.
- The human resource section identifies your team of family and staff that will implement your plan.
- The financial plan proves and supports the feasibility of your idea.
- The conclusion is where you recap the important points and ensures that the reader understands what it is that you want to say.
- The appendix contains supporting data such as resumes', supporting financial and market data, etc.
- Surveys of customers and suppliers.

1.4.7 How do I make my plan stand out?

How Do I make my plan stand out?

There are a number of things that you can do to make your business plan stand out with a reader. The following are a few ideas that work well.

- Try having a credible referral, a third party bring your plan to the attention of the reader. This is very important especially when looking for new investors.
- Create real world market associations with your products. Include a list of customers that want to purchase your product or service.
- Thoroughly research your business venture.
- Use charts and tables wherever possible. Make it simple for the reader. A picture is worth a thousand words.
- Have an idea that is unique and show that it creates a proprietary market advantage.
- Your plan is simple and to the point.
- Make a knowledgeable and credible presentation or pitch to the reader as a companion your plan.

1.4.8 10 essential tips for a successful business plan

10 essential tips for a successful business plan

The following are 10 essential tips for creating a successful business plan:

1. Have hands-on involvement in the creation of your plan and keep it simple.
2. Create a big picture vision. You need the end in mind.
3. Try to keep the plan between 20-30 pages.
4. Document your plan on paper so it can be shared with your family, and other relevant stakeholders.
5. Refer to your plan often and integrate the plan into the daily activities and operations of the farm.
6. Regularly update the plan as it is meant to be a living evolving document.
7. Use the planning activity to challenge your business, family and to continually raise the bar.
8. Be market, not product driven in your thinking and planning.
9. Be realistic in your financial scenarios. Use a best case, worse case and the most like scenario.
10. Know your plan inside and out. Practice your presentation and have the information down pat before the presentation. Anticipate likely questions and be prepared with answers.

1.5 Business planning warm up exercise

Business Planning Warm Up Exercise

This exercise can be done in advance of your planning exercise or as part of your planning exercise. The following warm up questions and discussion points will help your team condition and stretch their thinking in preparation for your business planning project. Some questions may not be relevant in all business planning situations.

Briefly discuss and answer the following questions.

Why do you need a business plan?

What type of business do you currently have?

Describe in one sentence what your business does well.

Outline a brief history of your business.

When did you start your business?

What was the original purpose of your business?

Who are the owners, what do they own and what is their role?

Do you have a business vision? What is it?

_____

_____

What are the businesses strengths and weaknesses?
Strengths: _____
Weaknesses: _____

What are the businesses opportunities and threats?
Opportunities: _____
Threats: _____

What are your major key business objectives?
Objective#1: _____
Objective#2: _____
Objective#3: _____

What have been your business successes and challenges to this point?

_____

_____

What products or services do you offer?

_____

_____

What are the unique benefits of your products or services?

_____

_____

Is the production of your different products dependant on one another?

_____

_____

Does one product open access to a market for the other?

Explain: _____

_____

Who is your customer?

What is the specific consumer need for your product or service?

How big is the market for your product or service?

How will you get a share of this market?

Your strategy?

How will you distribute your new products?

Who is the competition?

How will you promote your new products?

How will you finance your new product idea?

2.0 Creating a business plan

Creating a business plan

"It is essential to prepare a business plan for each new enterprise or opportunity that you're considering".

Andrew Stairs, Stairsholme Farm, Hemmingford, Quebec

The following sections outline what is in each part of a business plan. This will help you better understand what you need to include in your business plan. Templates of these pages are included in the accompanying CD-ROM.

2.1 The cover page

The cover needs to contain some basic information. The business plan title, the name of the farm, the period the plan covers and the date. It may also contain a confidentiality statement to limit the circulation of the plan.

2.2 The second page

The second page typically will have key contact information. List the contact information and person for the farm/ranch business as well as contact information of the preparer of the business plan especially if it is by an outside advisor. You may choose to add further statements of confidentially or recognition of risk on this page. These statements typically identify to the reader that the plan developed represents the management's best estimate of the future potential of the proposed business venture. They are used to make the reader aware that there maybe inherent risk associated with the plan and that a change in business circumstances could have an impact on the projections and assumptions of the plan. The following are some examples of these types of statements.

Example Confidentiality and Risk Statements

- **Example Confidentially Statement:** The information included in this plan is confidential and is provided on the understanding that it will not be disclosed to third parties without the written consent of _____.

- **Example Recognition of Risk:** This business plan represents our management's best estimate of future potential of the proposed business venture. It should be recognized that not all major risks can be accurately predicted and/or otherwise avoided and that few business plans are free from errors and omissions. Therefore the investor should be aware that this business plan has inherent risks that should be evaluated prior to their investment.

- **Typical Consultant Waiver:** This report has been prepared by _____ _____ on a best-effort basis and reflects the conditions prevailing at the time of our analysis from _____ to _____ 20____. The conclusions expressed in this report are to some degree based on assumptions and opinions, which are subject to variation due to the continuing evolution of the _____ farm business. Therefore, we cannot represent them as definite results, only as anticipated results if the opinions and assumptions evolve as anticipated and remain valid. In our opinion the facts represent a fair and accurate assessment of the _____ farm.

2.3   Table of contents

The table of contents is your navigational map around your business plan. Readers rely on the table of contents to quickly locate specific sections of interest to them. Make sure the headings are accurate and the pages are numbered correctly in the table of contents. Each reader has their own special interest in particular sections and may want to refer to them first. The following is a basic layout of a typical business plan table of contents. While your plan may very in its focus, it should include information organized under these main headings.

2.4   The executive summary

The executive summary is a key section to any plan. It is the first and possibly the only section of your plan that will get read. It is what sells your plan to the reader; it creates interest for your plan and your project, and stimulates the reader to read the entire plan. You rarely ever get a second chance to make a good first impression. Subsequent plans will always be slightly tainted

An executive summary is a brief summary of what is contained in your business plan. It must capture the readers attention and stimulate them to read on. by your first plan submission. It is therefore very important to get the plan right the first time. If you are not sure of your plan test it on others before approaching your final reader, investor or lender.

There are two schools of thought when it comes to the executive summary. One is that the executive summary is created after the plan is written. It becomes a summary for the entire report. The other line of thinking is to write the executive summary first and support it by the rest of the plan. Whichever methods you choose remember that the executive summary is key to gaining support for your project. Hint: Review your plans' executive summary; if doesn't captivate interest in your project then rewrite it until it does. Executive summaries should be no more than 2 pages long.

2.5   The business overview

The company overview contains tombstone data on the company, a brief company history and information on ownership.

Legal Description of the Business
Your company's legal form of business.

Legal business name:

The business is registered as:
- Sole Proprietorship ☐ , Partnership ☐ , Corporation ☐ , Co-operative ☐
- Registration # ——————— Date Registered ———————

When was the business formed? ————————————————————
Operating Location: ————————————————————

Ownership Structure Who are the legal owners?

NAME	SHARES

(Include resumes in the plan's appendices.)

The ownership structure is normally best presented in some form of organizational chart as in the example illustrated below. An organizational chart helps the reader sort out who has ownership control. Ownership structures can be complicated especially in large families or where some owners are absentee or nonworking owners.

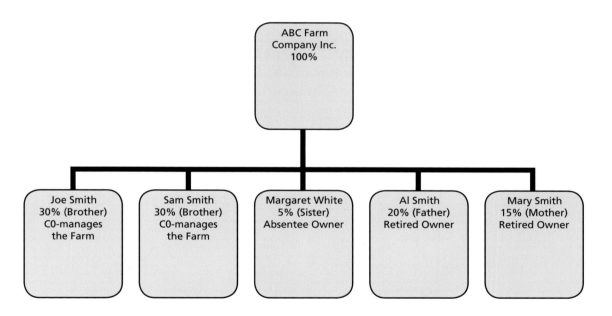

Board of Directors If you have a board; who is on your board of directors.

NAME	POSITION	YEARS ON BOARD

Important strategic alliances and partnerships

Outside Strategic Alliances and Partnerships - Strategic alliances can strengthen your business and bring credibility to a project. The risk is shared over more players. Alliances may be with other farmers and ranchers, cooperatives, marketing groups and clubs, suppliers, equipment manufactures, distributors or a related company. What other organizations do you have business agreements with and what is there relationship?

NAME	RELATIONSHIP

Succession Strategy – Your succession strategy proves that you are forward thinking. A succession plan also illustrates to a lender or investor when and to whom a transfer might occur.

In brief terms what is your succession strategy?

If you don't have a strategic plan when should it happen?

Business advisors and important contacts

BUSINESS ADVISORS	NAME	CONTACT #
Lawyer		
Accountant		
Bank		
Consultants		
Other Advisor		
Bookkeeper		

2.6 Your business vision, mission and key objectives

Your business vision, mission and key objectives

Your farm/ranch vision

It all starts with some one having a <u>vision</u>. You most likely have a vision for your farm/ranch business; you just may never have taken the time to write it down. There was;

o   an original driving reason that you started your business,
o   something that you wanted to achieve,
o   a burning desire, a motivating purpose that pulled you to farming;
o   **you had a vision!**

A strategic vision is big picture viewpoint, with a long-term timeframe. It may take your entire working life for you to achieve your business vision. Strategic visioning is determining where it is you want your business to be at a particular point in the future while considering the business environment around you. It is natural that your vision will evolve and change over time with your business circumstances and environment.

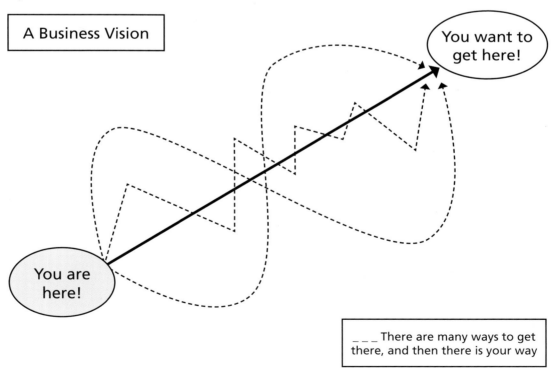

A Business Vision

You are here!

You want to get here!

_ _ _ There are many ways to get there, and then there is your way

Example Vision: To be the leading innovative producer of specialty carrot products in the country.
What is your vision? What do you want to achieve?

Your farm/ranch mission

Your business mission is basically a description of how you do business; it gives some parameters to your business operation. It is a statement that commonly captures the following information:

- **Why you are in business.** (What is your driving desire?)
- **What your business does.** (What product or service you produce or offer?)
- **Whom do you do it for?** (The customer segment you target.)
- **How do you do it?** (The technologies you use or method of sale, etc.)

(Hint: Your mission should be a statement that you and your team can believe in, support and embrace as a company.)

Example Mission: To create a viable sustainable farm/ranch business that continually offers innovative carrot products to our target markets while creating the highest value for our family.
First Draft Mission Statement:
Second Draft Mission Statement:
Third Draft Mission Statement:
Final Mission Statement:

Your key objectives

Your key objectives or goals are actions that you must undertake to achieve your vision and mission. An objective is normally "to do" something. Hint: When setting objectives use "to" plus an "action verb".

Example Objective: To reduce our maintenance costs on our farm this year by 10%.
Objective #1
Objective #2
Objective #3
Objective #4
Objective #5

2.7   SWOT analysis

The acronym SWOT stands for strengths, weaknesses, opportunities and threats. A SWOT analysis is typically done as a scan of your business operating environment. It is a way to determine if you are overlooking anything that is important to your business future and identify anything that might jeopardize or blindside your project. Business strengths and weaknesses are normally looked at from an internal point of view while opportunities and threats are analyzed from an external vantage point.

By examining your internal strengths and weaknesses, and your external opportunities and threats you will better understand the capabilities of your business. Once you recognize what you have and are up against you can then develop strategies of how to minimize your weaknesses and threats and how to maximize your strengths and opportunities. The SWOT analysis is also a great business management tool to help you realize what your business is and is not. (Hint: This is a great activity to involve stakeholders to build support for your project.)

Internal strengths

Internal strengths are internal factors or situations within your business that could potentially affect your company in a positive (+) way. Fill out the worksheet to create a complete list of the internal strengths that your business has at present.

	INTERNAL STRENTGHS	
Strengths	**Description of Strengths**	**Ways (options) to maximize the strengths.**
Example: Our land produces early crops.	We have an unique microclimate that produces early crops at least a week ahead of other farms in the area.	Could we adopt new technology that would further increase the early crop advantage, so that we could produce more and higher value crops?
1.		
2.		
3.		

Internal weaknesses

Internal weaknesses are internal factors or situations that currently could potentially affect your company in a negative (-) way. Fill out the worksheet to create a complete list of the internal weaknesses your business has currently.

	INTERNAL WEAKNESSES	
Weakness	**Description of Weakness**	**Ways (options) to minimize the weakness.**
Example: We have no succession strategy for the farm/ranch if something unexpected should happen to dad or mom.	In the event of a tragedy with no succession strategy the farm's future will be at risk and may have to be sold.	Start the process immediately with all family stakeholders to develop a feasible succession strategy for our farm/ranch business.
1.		
2.		
3.		

External opportunities

External opportunities are outside or external factors or situations that could potentially affect your company in a positive (+) way. Fill out the worksheet to create a complete list of the external opportunities your business potential could have available in the future.

EXTERNAL OPPORTUNITIES		
Opportunity	Description of Opportunity	Ways (options) to maximize the opportunity to your business.
Example: The neighbours land unexpectedly comes for sale.	You need land to expand for the future and land next to your farm rarely comes up for sale.	Develop a business plan to illustrate to a lender how the farm will use the new land to be more sustainable in the future.
1.		
2.		
3.		

External threats

External threats are outside or external factors or situations that could potentially affect your company in a negative (-) way. Fill out the worksheet to create a complete list of the external threats your business potential could face.

EXTERNAL THREATS		
Threat	Description of Threat	Ways (options) to minimize the threat to your business.
Example: Your buyer introduces new food safety protocol to be implemented within two years.	If your farm doesn't comply you will risk loosing a major market for your crops.	Identify required training courses; comply early (within one year) to ensure that you retain your markets.
1.		
2.		
3.		

2.8 The project need (purpose)

What often is forgotten in the development of a business plan is stating clearly what it is you are looking for from the reader. You don't want the reader after having read your plan to be shaking his/her head wondering what your project is and what it is that you are asking for. State what it is that you want from the reader of your business plan.

Funds requested and their intended use

Example: **Funds Requested and Their Intended Use**

The owners are requesting a loan of $140,000. The funds will be used for the following business activities:

- Build a new carrot processing barn $90,000
- Purchase grading processing equipment $25,000
- Purchase a walk in freezer/cooler $ 25,000

The owners are requesting the following terms from the bank for both the immediate and long-term loans.

- 15 year mortgage using the land as security
- Interest rate of prime plus 1.5%
- Annual amortized payments of $13,000 year
- Annual pay out privileges of 10% of the principal

(Note: Include quotations for the construction and equipment in the appendix.)

2.9 The marketing plan

Without a market for your product or service there is little need for you to produce anything. A potential market is only a potential market until you can supply the products and services in a way that satisfies the needs and demands of that particular market.

The purpose of the marketing plan

The market analysis is meant to validate the opportunity for your product or service in the marketplace. Marketing is often described in terms of the four "P's"; Product, Price, Place and Promotion.

A market analysis should answer the following questions;

- Who will buy your **product or service**, why and how much?
- What **price** will the market pay and at what profit margin to you?
- How you intend to distribute your product or service to the market**place**?
- How you will **promote** your product or service to that intended market?

Marketing is the process of understanding the customer's needs, producing products to meet those needs, delivering those products to the market and making a profit for your business in the process. There is little sense in going through the expense and the process of producing a product or service, only to find that there is a limited, or worse, no market. Build your market before you produce your products and build the factory!

Different commodities will potentially have different requirements from a marketing plan. For example in a supply managed commodity the markets are pre-established and little analysis is required in this area. The markets can also be predetermined by the available processors and manufacturers within a reasonable transportation distance from your farm/ranch operation. It is important to keep in mind that there are many pathways and variations to the market both direct and indirect. The pathway you choose in your market chain determines the profit level you receive for your products and services. Every function in the market chain has a cost and benefit. If you want the added benefit you have to incur an added cost. The cost must therefore be less than the benefit to make performing the market chain function worthwhile to your business.

The diagram below illustrates many of the market options and channels that producers have to the marketplace.

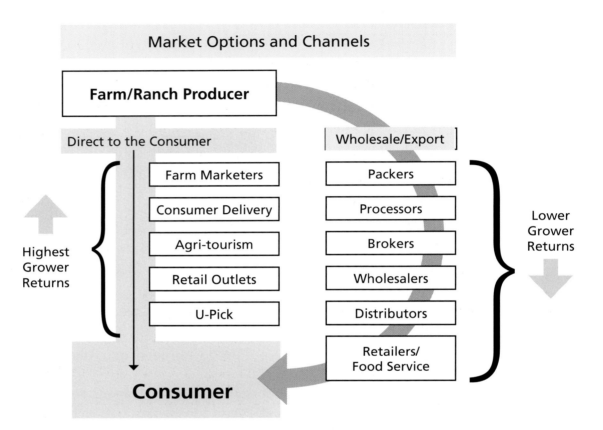

Market Options and Channels

Farm/Ranch Producer

Direct to the Consumer

Wholesale/Export

Farm Marketers	Packers
Consumer Delivery	Processors
Agri-tourism	Brokers
Retail Outlets	Wholesalers
U-Pick	Distributors
	Retailers/Food Service

Highest Grower Returns

Lower Grower Returns

Consumer

MHA, ProAgri ©2003

General market opportunity warm up questions

1. Why is this product or service a market opportunity for our business?
2. What is the potential of this market? What is the risk?
3. Will we need to invest in advertising and promotion?
4. What packaging is necessary?
5. Would we have a competitive advantage?
6. Can we devote the necessary time?
7. Does this market opportunity allow us to achieve our farm goals and objectives?
8. Do I have the resources necessary to develop this market opportunity?
9. Is the opportunity timely? What is the time frame?
10. Can we be price competitive and still be profitable?
11. Can we produce the quality and quantity the market demands?
12. Will the market continue to grow?
13. How do we minimize our risk and maximize the opportunity?
14. What channel would we use to move the product or services to market?

Answering the following questions will help you describe your marketing strategy and plan.

Who will buy your product or service, why and for how much?

Describe the general marketplace for your product or service.

What are the industry and market trends that are relevant to your situation?

What is the profile of the market (customer) that you are targeting?

Who is your competition?
How is your product or service positioned relative to the competition? Do you have an advantage?

What are the market risks to your business? (Typically risks are political or external factors and issues that can affect your markets. For example: interest rates, new regulations, imported goods, environmental factors, Canadian dollar value, international incident and embargos could all impact your opportunities in your markets.)

What share of the market do you currently have and what is possible in the future? Explain.

Do you have an export strategy?

What is your pricing strategy? How do you set your prices? What price are markets willing to pay and at what is your profit margin?
Is your price competitive? Is there flexibility in your pricing strategy?

How will you distribute your product or service to the marketplace? What are your distribution channels?
What certifications or standards of production are required from your markets?

How will you promote your product or service to the intended market? What is your promotion strategy and budget?
Do you have a brand? Describe?

Most readers of a business plan are seasoned or experienced at reading plans. One of the quick evaluations readers often use when examining your business plan is to look at your market sales verses return (margin) projections. They will gauge your sales/return projections against what typically makes business sense with the reader's knowledge of your industry.

For example: If your plans projections shows low sales volumes and low returns (margins) red flags will likely go up questioning your market opportunity or your marketing knowledge, ability and skills. Low returns (margins) generally require larger sales volumes to cover the overhead; operating costs and return a profit. Higher margins allow you to cover your overhead and profit with much smaller sales volumes. The best case scenario is to have high sales volumes of a product or service that has high returns. Your projected sales volumes and returns need to be realistic and be substantiated in your plan. Check where your business fits in the matrix below.

Volume / Returns Marketing Matrix

	Low Volume (Sales)	High Volume (Sales)
Low Returns (Margins)	Worst Case Scenario for Any Farm Ranch Business	Good Case Scenario for Large Land Base Farms
High Returns (Margins)	Good Case Scenario for Small Land Base Farms	Best Case Scenario for Any Farm Ranch Business

2.10 The product or service

The product or service

Many business plans are based around the development of a new product, service. The reader may be unfamiliar with your product or service, so it is important to give them a good understanding of what you will be producing or the service that you are offering

Describe your product or service.

Describe what makes your product or service unique. What is the unique advantage of the product? What makes it different from the competition?

What are the risks of producing this product or offering this service?
What are the barriers to success of our farm/ranch producing this product or offering this service?

What are the volumes of this product that you can produce in year one, two and so on?

2.11 The production plan

The production plan

The purpose of the operational plan

The operational plan or production plan outlines the process required to produce your products and services. It will illustrate that your business has the necessary resources, skills, knowledge and abilities to undertake your project.

Current Land Owned: List the land and property assets that you own.

Description of Land/ Property	Owned/ Leased	Rent/Yr	Acres/ Hectares	Cultivated or Wooded	$Original Value	$Market Value	Taxes/ Yr

Equipment Inventory: List the equipment that you currently own.

Description of Equipment	Owned/ Leased	Year Purchased	$ Cost

Describe your current production facilities?
Describe your current production process? Include a diagram if possible.
Describe your proposed new production facilities. New buildings, equipment or renovations required?
(Note: Include plans for new construction or renovations in the appendix.)
What is the timeline schedule for any new construction?
(Note: See sample construction schedule on accompanying CD.)

Outline how your business relates to an environmental farm/ranch plan.

2.12 The human resource plan

The human resource plan

The purpose of the human resource plan

Human resources can be a very challenging aspect of managing a business operation. Labour expenses will be among the highest individual costs to your business in a given production season or year. Your human resources are often the most difficult item to budget for and manage. Labour issues especially on larger farm/ranch businesses typically consume a large amount of a manager's time.   There is only so much you can do yourself, there are only so many hours in a day, your business can't grow without help from other good people.   Whether your human resources are available from your family or from outside the farm, a human resource plan reduces stress, confusion, and problems. Your ability to manage your human resources is a key indicator of your ability to manage your entire farm ranch/operation. Moving into new business opportunities may require the development of new skills and the hiring of new staff. You should also identify necessary skills training programs for your staff during the scope of the business plan.

> **Key Staff** - You can't do everything yourself. Who are the key staff and family members that will help you achieve your goals and what roles and skills do they bring to the business? For example your daughter and son may run the farm market and your key hand manages the field production.

Name	Position	Time in Position	Function

(You may want to include resumes of key staff in your appendices.)

How many staff do you have, need and when?
What are your seasonal requirements?

How do you plan to find new staff, and retain existing staff to create long-term stability?

What new skills will we need to learn? Where will we obtain this knowledge?

Organizational Chart (Team)
What is your organizational structure and what is the chain of accountability? Who reports to whom?

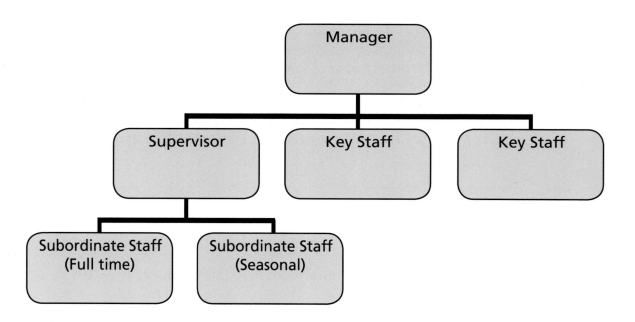

2.13 The financial plan

The purpose of the financial plan

The financial section of the plan needs to demonstrate the financial viability of the proposed project and the overall financial impact any changes will have on the business. This section presents summaries of your business history, financial projections, key financial assumptions and how you established them, debt servicing requirements and your capital project requirements.

Projected financial plan

The financial projections will reflect the goals and objectives that you set in the previous sections. They are the foundation for proving the viability of your product or service. Financial projections help you to validate a market opportunity or project on your farm and prove that it will be profitable and necessary. Is the concept feasible, sustainable? The financial statements model your business in the way that you envision it in the future. They are your test run before the rubber hits the road. Forecasting your businesses financial statements and capital requirements are referred to as projections or proforma statements.

What are financial statements?

The financial statements are standardized accounting formats recognized by accountants and lenders for recording business activities and transactions. The normally accepted financial statements are made up of three key components.

1. Income Statement
2. Cash Flow Statement
3. The Balance Sheet

1. Income statement

An income / expense statement, sometimes called a statement of operations, provides the profit performance summary of the business activities. This statement summarizes the sales (revenue) and expenses over a period of time and measures the manager's ability to make a profit from the resources available. Cash based income statements do not provide an accurate reflection of the businesses performance because accounts payable and accounts receivable are not included in the calculations nor are inventory changes accounted for. Adjusting your cash statements to accrual is required to ensure the statements provide an accurate reflection of the profitability of the business for a period of time. Understanding the connection between the cash flow, income and expenses and the balance sheet is imperative to operating a successful business. The impact of management decisions on the financial position of the business is critical to understand. Managers need to know that decisions relating to cash flow could either contribute to or be detrimental to the profitability of the business. Financing decisions could equally affect cash flow and profitability.

INCOME	20____	20____	20____
Crop / Product Sales			
Livestock Sales			
Subsidies and Grants			
Other Income			
Changes in Crop/Livestock Inventory			
Changes in receivables			
TOTAL INCOME ($)			
PRODUCTION EXPENSES			
Fertilizer/Seed			
Purchased Feed			
Livestock			
Pesticides			
Other Production Exp.			
Total Production Exp. ($)			
Contribution Margin ($)			
OTHER EXPENSES			
Advertising/Marketing			
Amortization			
Fuel, Oil, Gas			
Machinery R & M			
Building R & M			
Freight / Trucking			
Insurance(Liability/fire)			
Vehicle Exp. (ins.,fuel,R&M)			
Machinery / Eqpt. Lease			
Op.Interest and S / C			
Long Term Interest			
Office Supplies			
Professional Fees			
Memberships and dues			
Small Tools / Supplies			
Taxes			
Wages and Benefits			
Utilities			
Travel			
Vet, Drugs and Breeding			
Miscellaneous			
Total Other Expenses ($)			
Net Farm Income ($)			

Income Statement

(Projected Income /Expense 20___ - 20___)
Your business plan will often include projections for a period of 1-3 years. The items will vary slightly with different commodities and types of business operations.

2. Cash flow statement

Most people in the agricultural industry have often heard the saying "cash flow is king" from lenders, producers, and accountants. The importance of cash flow cannot be overlooked when preparing a business plan for the farm. Cash inflow and outflow is the heart of any business regardless of the equity position. Inadequate cash flow is often the most serious problem facing a new business. Another favorite remark is "you can't eat equity", which means that even if you have little or no debt, cash is required to meet the day to day obligations of the business.

A cash flow tells you when and how much money is received or spent during each measurement period (weekly, monthly, quarterly). This is critical for determining how much operating loan is required, for determining debt repayment scheduling, for scheduling capital improvements and to access funds for other uses from the business. What a cash flow will not tell you is if the business is profitable or what the financial position of the business is at the end of the year.

The first 2-3 years cash flow is very important for a new business. It helps to evaluate the impact of a new venture on the existing business and provides valuable information for determining the debt structuring and repayment plans. Many times producers attempt to finance a new venture from cash flow that leads to over runs on their operating loans and jeopardizes both the new and the existing business.

Cash flow projections are also very useful for evaluating the progress of a new venture. Monitoring the projected cash inflow and cash outflow on a regular basis provides an opportunity to re-evaluate plans throughout the year rather than waiting until year end only to find out changes should have been made in month 4. Cash flow projections provide a guide with which to benchmark and compare against actual results.

3. The balance sheet verses the net worth statement

The financial position of your farm business at a point in time can be best presented in a balance sheet or net worth statement. For many farms a balance sheet, prepared based on the cost base of the assets or depreciated value of assets, does not provide an accurate assessment of net worth. In order to more accurately determine the equity of a farm, a net worth statement should be prepared. This statement reflects the market value of the assets. The only difference between a net worth statement and a balance sheet is the method of valuing the assets. A net worth statement reflects any inflation or deflation of business assets. When analyzing a businesses' performance it is important to recognize why the equity position has changed. Equity increase or decrease could be strictly due to a change in market value rather than business performance.

A balance sheet will provide the financial progress of the business for the previous 12 months as well as provide the information required to determine many of the key financial ratios used to evaluate the financial position of the business. The current ratio, liquidity and solvency of a business can be determined as well as debt to equity ratio. An accurate balance sheet can provide much needed information for determining the viability of a new enterprise as well as provide lenders with information regarding your financial management abilities. Balance sheets are also very useful in estate and succession planning.

Projected Balance Sheet

You will normally be asked to supply a 3 year projected balance sheet in your business plan.

Date: _____	Opening Balance	Year 1	Year 2	Year 3
Assets ($)				
Cash				
Accounts Receivable				
Inventory- livestock, crops & supplies				
Pre-paids / other				
Land				
Machinery / equipment				
Buildings				
Quota				
Investments / other				
Total Assets ($)				
Liabilities ($)				
Operating loan				
Payables & Accruals				
Income Tax payable				
Current portion of long term debt				
Short term debt				
Long term debt				
Shareholder loans				
Total Liabilities ($)				
Shareholders' Equity ($)				
Capital				
Retained earnings				
Total Liabilities & Equity ($)				

Other useful financial planning tools

1. Partial Budgets

Partial budgeting is a tool used to estimate the financial impact on the overall farm operation of the addition of a new enterprise or changes to an existing enterprise. This tool looks only at the new sources of revenue created and increase/decrease of operating and fixed costs to determine the impact on the existing business. A partial budget considers the added or lost revenues, reduced or added costs and the net effect they will have on the existing business. Partial budgeting also includes non-economic pros and cons of a business decision such as improved safety for workers, more family time, increased efficiency in operations and other non-cash expenses or improvements.

Partial budgeting is a very important business tool for producers who are considering starting a new venture or diversifying their core farm business. Used in conjunction with the other financial statements for the farm, a consolidated projection can be created to determine the impact on cash flow, profitability and long term financial position of the farm. The partial budget compares:

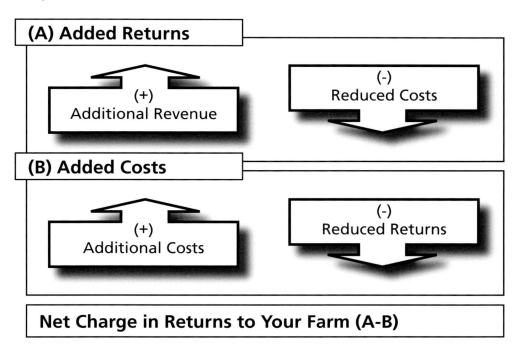

(A) Added Returns

(+)
Additional Revenue

(-)
Reduced Costs

(B) Added Costs

(+)
Additional Costs

(-)
Reduced Returns

Net Charge in Returns to Your Farm (A-B)

2. Break even analysis

A break-even analysis is used to determine the level of sales required to operate the business where total expenses are equal to total income. If you produce more sales than required for the break-even position you will make money, and if you produce less sales you will lose money. In new agricultural business ventures, producers should determine their break-even position. Using this tool you can determine what the price per unit sold needs to be to cover the operating costs and the fixed costs for the business. Knowing your break-even cost can provide valuable information for negotiating price and profits for the business. Without knowing what a product costs to produce, pricing is often reduced to levels which are not sustainable for the business.

The break-even position is calculated by determining the contribution margin available from the sale of each production unit. Contribution margin (CM) is calculated as selling price minus variable costs (SP – VC). Fixed costs (FC) are also determined for the facilities, administration, interest, depreciation, taxes, insurance and repairs. The breakeven number of units to be produced is equal to the fixed costs divided by the contribution margin. (# Units = FC/CM) The breakeven revenue ($) required is equal to the break-even # units x selling price ($).

Break Even Sales Analysis

$$\frac{\text{TOTAL FIXED COSTS}}{\text{(REVENUE / UNIT – VARIABLE COST/UNIT)}} = \text{BREAK EVEN POINT (Units Required)}$$

Scenario	20__	20__	20__	20__
Fixed Costs				
Revenue/Unit				
Variable Unit Cost				
Units Required to Break Even				

3. Sensitivity analysis

Sensitivity analysis is a tool used to demonstrate the impact of a change in price received or a change in expenses. This tool provides a matrix that evaluates multiple scenarios related to increases or decreases in price per unit as well as increases or decreases in cost per unit produced. It is used to determine the risks associated with market price fluctuations as well as risks associated with input expenses. Typically a sensitivity analysis looks at the best case, worst case and most probable case scenarios.

Financing alternatives

There are basically two ways to finance any business; debt financing and equity financing. Often producers do not spend sufficient time looking for or utilizing the proper type of financing or financing mix to ensure a new venture has sufficient capital to be successful.

Debt financing (borrow the money) is the most common method used. This means the loan will have to be repaid over a period of time and typically requires a security agreement associated with a group of assets. The lender receives payment of interest for risking their money in your business venture. Debt financing does not provide ownership rights to the business.

Equity financing refers to any money that you or a business associate would invest directly into the business. Equity contributions result in some degree of ownership in the new business in return for making the contribution. Many farmers are not comfortable with outside ownership and therefore prefer to debt finance.

The difficulty in only using debt financing is the ability of the business to service the debt. Many farm businesses require significant contributions of capital which cannot be supported through debt financing alone. A mix of debt and equity financing is often required to provide sufficient security for the lenders as well as ensuring that the new venture can service the debt.

Sources of equity can include personal savings, investments by friends and relatives, employee investment or other venture capital provided through venture capital funds or business partners. To attract equity investment from others into your business, you must be willing to share some of the ownership as well as some of the profits of the business. You must also be prepared to allow for management input from investors if they wish to participate in the operation. When outside equity or debt financing is provided, those investors and lenders will most likely want a business plan and periodic reporting of results against your business plan.

Obtaining financing

Financing for farm businesses is in many cases difficult to obtain. It will depend on your current financial position, your track record with lenders and the presentation of a viable business plan. Many enterprises may not have a proven history and be considered too risky for the commercial lender.

On farms with a large asset base and existing cash flow, you can leverage your main farm enterprise to finance the new venture. This provides a unique advantage over those individuals starting from scratch. It may be tempting to use your existing credit facilities and operating loan to finance the new business, but this could put both enterprises at risk.

The most common methods of financing are from savings, personal lines of credit, supplier credit and supplier short term investments. Regardless of the source, you need to ensure you can provide a viable business plan which outside interests can understand and support.

Loan information

In addition to the principle three financial statements, your business plan will need to include detail on your existing loans and your projected financing requirements. Separate each type of loan per item along with balances, interest rates and payment schedules.

Capital Purchase Summary:

Item	Sales/Trade In	Purchases	Cash Down	Required Financing	Expected Life	CCA/ Depreciation
Intermediate Assets						
New Tractor						
New Harrow						
Long-term Assets						
New Equipment shed						
10 Hectares Land						

Loan Summary (Existing and Projected):

Loan Description	Original Amount	Amount Owing	Interest Rate %	Payment Frequency	Annual Payment	Principle	Interest	Lender	Security	Term Years
Intermediate Assets										
Operating Loan										
Tractor Loan										
Long-term Assets										
Mortgage										
Projected										
New Barn										

Risk

Risk is defined as a circumstance that could endanger or put in jeopardy a business venture. The level of risk a person is willing to take depends on many things, not the least of which is the chance an idea will not succeed. Risk evaluation is essential in order to not jeopardize the success of the business. Farm diversification in itself is considered a method to reduce risk associated with price fluctuations, market risk and weather related risks.

The level of risk a business takes is in direct proportion to the level of reward realized from the success of the business venture. If a producer feels there is no risk involved, there is likely no reward either. A calculated risk will require a thorough evaluation of the pros and cons of an idea and risk assessment to determine the "what if" scenarios. There are many different programs and opportunities to protect against some of the risks (insurance, CAIS, diversification).

As with any business or idea there are uncontrollable and unforeseen risks that can impact a project. The best you can do is understand the risks which you can control or mitigate and continuously monitor the marketplace to identify potential risks as you progress with your business.

2.14 The conclusion

The conclusion

The conclusion is the opportunity to recap what the plan is all about and how the different sections interact and interrelate for the reader. It is the chance to reiterate your objectives and what is desired from the reader. This is normally summed up in a short paragraph.

2.15 The appendix

The appendix

The appendix can be at the end of the plan or its own separate companion document. As a companion document it allows the reader to refer to reference information without having to flip back and forth. Common information found in the appendix of a business plan includes:

- Resumes of Owners & Key People
- Financial Information and Data
- Market Information
- Permits Certificates
- Building Plans
- Quotations
- Other Supporting Information

3.0 Profiles of planners

Profiles of planners

"Send us a new map;
we have marched off of the old one."

A Roman Military General's Dispatch to Cesar

The following are mini profiles of farm business that have been successful over time using business planning. The businesses have used planning at different phases of their business life cycles for different reasons. These are brief insights into businesses that believe in the value of business planning.

3.1 The Van Dyk Family Farm

The Van Dyk Family Farm

Van Dyk Blueberry Enterprises Ltd. / **Van Dyk's Health Juice Products Ltd.**
Caledonia, Queens County, Nova Scotia
http://www.vandykblueberries.ca

Case and Riek Van Dyk have been farming in Caledonia, Nova Scotia since 1956 when they emigrated from Holland. Originally a dairy farm, the business evolved over time into a hog and blueberry farm. The hog operation called

Onf Gen Oegon Farms Ltd. was separated in 1999 and purchased by sons Gerald and Peter. Today Case and Riek operate Van Dyk Blueberry Enterprises Ltd. a fresh pack wild blueberry processing business and Van Dyk's Health Juice Products Ltd. a unique value added processing enterprise producing wild blue berry juice. The current wild blueberry farm operation (Van Dyk Health Blueberry Enterprises Ltd.) consists of approximately 500 acres of production land plus 416 acres of woodlot/forest land and an approximately 5,000 sq. ft. blueberry processing / juice manufacturing facility. Case and Riek in their seventies are now looking to business planning to assist them in their succession planning and passing the businesses on to their seven children.

Message for the Reader from Case Van Dyk:

1. **Why do you prepare and utilize business plans?**

   In theory it is a road map to guide us to where we want to go and to ensure that we have all of our resources in place. The reality is that a business plan is normally done because someone like a lender has asked for it.

2. **How do you utilize plans for operations and management of your farm businesses?**

   The need for business plans has increased as our businesses have become more complex. The market for hogs is a roller coaster ride and business planning has been critical to minimize costly errors and mistakes in production. When we moved into wild blueberry fresh pack processing we needed a business plan to evaluate and analyze the new investments verses market opportunity. We use business planning more in our value added business because the market opportunities are continually evolving and we need to know the impact of expansion to service new markets. We are now looking at farm succession and will need more business planning.

3. **What benefits do you get for planning?**

   Comfort, peace of mind, that we are doing the right thing and have things well thought out. That we are not unduly risking what we have spent many years developing.

4. **What words of advice or recommendations can you offer to other producers in regards to business planning?**

   Use your business plan as much as possible. An annual business plan with quarterly review would be ideal. We use outside advisors to help us develop our plans. This is due to limited resources and time in house. Outside resources give us another perspective, another set of eyes looking at what we are doing. They can ask tough questions and force us to ensure our actions are congruent with our budgets and core strategic goals.

3.2 The Vantreight Family Farm

The Vantreight Family Farm

The Vantreight's / **A Daffodil Dynasty**
G.A. Vantreight and Sons, Saanich Peninsula, Vancouver Island, British Columbia
http://daffodil.com/

The Vantreight family farm started in 1891 by Geoff Vantreight Sr. operated as a berry and orchard farm specializing in strawberries, blueberries, cherries, apples and plums. In 1928 the first crop of daffodils was cultivated; little realizing the family would become world renowned for producing this flower. Geoff Jr. started farming in his teens with a great deal of drive and ambition and had soon expanded to 90 acres of crops including 30 acres of daffodils. Over a casual luncheon in 1956 with a group of volunteers from the

Cancer Society of Toronto, the future would be changed. The distribution of fresh daffodils from their farm represents the future of hope in order to find a cure for cancer around the world.

Today, the farm is operated by Ian and Michael along with several other family members. The crops include cut daffodils, tulips, iris and narcissus, as well as gladiolas and sunflowers. Diversification of products and working with farms in other countries is seen as a critical part of the continued expansion and growth of the farm. To remain viable, planning for the best utilization of financing and our capital is paramount. Also, working with others and building relationships has never been so important to the successful diversification of a business, especially a family farm. Business planning has played an important role in the success of the Vantreight family farm through the generations.

Message for the Reader from Ian Vantreight:

1. **Why do you prepare and utilize business plans?**

   So that everyone, from our Management Team down to our part time labourer knows at least the basics right up to the deals of what, when and why we are doing what we do.

2. **How do you utilize plans for operations and management of your farm businesses?**

   As a basis to bring details and substance to our Goals / Purpose / Mission / Vision for our farm.

3. **What benefits do you get for planning?**

   Clarity for me and my staff of our joint path.

4. **What words of advice or recommendations can you offer to other producers in regards to business planning?**

   The old adage is so true and I have experienced it many times, "When I fail to plan, I am planning to fail." Plan and be clear on where you want to go. How you get there is the exciting part you get do with your staff to set out the steps to that path to your create and fulfill Goal / Purpose / Mission / Vision for your operation.

The Schurman Family Farm

Schurman Farm Ltd. and **Spring Valley Farm Market**
Kensington, Prince Edward Island
www.springvalleyselect.com

The Schurman family farm grew from the early 1970's and rapidly in the late 1980's and early 1990's under the direction of Lea Schurman. The next

generation, Marc, took over in 1997 after graduating from the Nova Scotia Agricultural College. At that time the farm consisted of 450 sows; farrow to finish, and 250 beef cattle. When Marc came back to the farm operation, the hog industry was going through rough times and experienced some of the lowest prices ever. The lack of a positive return and the desire to become less risk adverse led to planning initiatives to explore other opportunities that could allow the farm to focus less on commodity production. Marc undertook extensive research and business planning efforts and in 2001 the decision was made to diversify the farm into greenhouse vegetable production. The greenhouse and wood boilers were added in late 2001, with the first crop ready for picking in early spring 2002. The product from this new facility was sold through the supermarkets, a variety of local small vendors and directly to local consumers via a roadside stand on the farm property. Planning expectations were not met in the greenhouse and it proved to be a challenge given the small scale of the operation and the lack of local expertise. In order to help rectify this lack of success and build upon past successes the farm undertook two new initiatives in 2003; (1) the planning and development of an expansion in the form of a retail farm market and (2) Marc undertook extensive management training with the CTEAM (Canadian Total Excellence in Agricultural Management), a course offered by the George Morris Center. In May 2004 Spring Valley Farm Market was opened in the nearby town of Kensington to tie all of the farm operations together with a market that would retail and wholesale fresh and processed pork and beef cuts along with the farm's greenhouse produce, other local produce and complementary items. Marc Schurman emphasizes that ongoing and extensive business planning has lessened the chance of surprises and heightened the chance of success for the Schurman Family Farm.

Message for the Reader from Marc Schurman:

1. **Why do you prepare and utilize business plans?**

   Through 1999 to 2001 I undertook extensive research to investigate how the farming operation could stabilize incomes and mitigate risk.

2. **How do you utilize plans for operations and management of your farm businesses?**

   Our plan was not merely for lenders, but a plan which convinced me, the primary operator that it could be done and included the details on how. The plan needed to include the traditional costs, cash flows and production predictions yet this plan would also incorporate more detailed analysis behind the numbers along with human resource planning, training, and production practices that would be implemented.

3. **What benefits do you get for planning?**

   It was my feeling that no amount of planning could ever be too much because no matter how much planning is done you will never foresee all events that may occur.

4. **What words of advice or recommendations can you offer to other producers in regards to business planning?**

   Overall, Schurman Farm Ltd.'s experience has been that where extensive planning has taken place, the chance of surprises was lessened and thus the chance of success heightened. Where I have experienced failure or lack of success, I can attribute it to lack of proper planning, training and by failing to use my strategic plan as a "living document" that grows and adapts as the business changes.

4.0 Using your business plan
Using your business plan

"Capital flows to profit.
A business plan that shows
sustainable profit attracts capital."

Ian Blenkharn, CFO, Willowdale Group of Farms, Berwick, NS

4.1 Presentation basics
Presentation basics

Once you have created your business plan you will want to take action on the initiatives in your plan. Simply mailing your plan to the intended reader is not enough. In most cases you will have to present or pitch your plan to either lenders, investors or your family and staff to garner their support for your project. If you started involving these stakeholders early in the planning process you may already have their support. If not, you will need to convince them to support your plan. It is time to prepare to pitch your business plan.

How you pitch your plan is almost as important as what you write in your plan. First impressions do count and you will rarely get a second chance to make a good first impression. While you need to show passion for your venture, it should not overshadow your presentation. The pitch should be in a professional manner, clearly stated, well organized and to the point. A presentation allows you to emphasize and highlight the points that you want to make without having to going through the entire business plan document. You can add detail as necessary and as questions are asked. A presentation also lets your audience get to know you. If you know your plan inside and out you will have the necessary knowledge to confidently pitch it to a lender,

investor, supplier, partner or member of the family. In most cases a verbal presentation will be all that is necessary. However, your presentation may benefit from visual aids if the project is complicated or has aspects that are difficult to understand. Your presentation/pitch will be a determining factor in obtaining support for your plan.

4.2 Pitching your plan

Pitching your plan

You should be able to verbally present your plan in a few minutes paralleling what is included in your written plan. Remember to keep your pitch short and to the point. Limit your presentation to approximately 20 minutes or less so that you leave lots of time for questions. A good presenter makes their key points and then allows time for questions. It is helpful to visualize pitching your plan a few times for practice prior to presentation day. Try it on out on your family or friends for practice. Just as when writing the business plan, customize your presentation and pitch according to your audience.

The following are some tips from lenders on how to make a good first impression.

1. Have multiple copies of your plan with you. (2-3 should suffice).
2. Content is more important than style or a fancy report.
3. Come prepared; know your plan inside and out.
4. Be on time for your appointment.
5. Dress appropriately for the scope of your project.
6. Present your own plan.
7. Respect peoples time, be concise and to the point, no fluff.
8. Don't de afraid to identify the risks and how your will overcome them.

The following are some tips when presenting/pitching your plan to lenders, investors or your family.

Tips when pitching to a lender

Lenders today, manage many accounts, time is important to them and they have specific lending criteria which they are looking for. Your lender is primarily interested in your assets, your ability to repay a loan, your management skills and abilities and whether your plan is realistic. They want to be assured and have confidence in you. Your history with lenders goes along way in obtaining their support. Highlight your track record, the merits of your project, your team and your management skills.

Tips when pitching to an outside investor

Pitching to an outside investor is a bit different than from pitching to a lender. An investor will be taking an ownership stake in your business; they will become your partner and are looking for good reasons to invest their money. While they may not be active in the daily decisions, they will surely be interested in your success, the businesses profit potential, return on investment and how they will eventually get their investment back. Investors review many plans and also have specific investment criteria. Third party introductions are helpful and can build confidence with outside investors prior to your presentation. Emphasize the growth and profit potential associated with your project.

Tips when pitching to your family.

Pitching to your family can often be your most difficult sell. It can be particularly difficult if you don't currently have good and open communication with your family. Your family knows you, your capabilities and track record better than anyone. Basically, your family wants open communication; to know what is going on, how business changes will impact them and their future. Make your pitch honest, open and to the point and make sure to leave lots of time for discussion and questions.

4.3 Implementing your plan

Don't let your business plan gather dust. If your plan is to be your guide, then you need to use it and integrate the actions into your daily business activities and operations. One of the best ways to integrate your plan into the daily activities of your business is to share it with the people that can and will be helping you to reach your goals; your family and staff. Meet regularly to discuss and evaluate progress. You may find it useful to ask of your team the following three questions in regards to business plan actions; (1) what is going well, (2) what are the concerns and (3) what adjustments do we need to make? Outline the important steps, priorities, timelines, budgets and milestones for your project and monitor against a budget. Taking action it is the surest way to integrate your business plan into your daily farm/ranch business operations.

5.0 Appendix

Appendix

The following information may be found useful in the development a business plan for your farm/ranch operation. This is not an endorsement for any organization or product listed below.

5.1 CFBMC website references

CFBMC website references

The Canadian Farm Business Management Council (CFBMC) website offers a catalogue of many useful farm business management tools and publications. **http://www.farmcentre.com**

5.2 Financial institution business planning links

Financial institution business planning links

The following financial institution websites offer useful business planning information. There are some examples, business plan templates and even business plan creators.

VISA
http://www.visa.ca/smallbusiness/

FCC Farm Credit Canada
http://www.fcc-fac.ca/en/LearningCentre/business_plan_e.asp
main=4&sub1=managementnews&sub2=businessplan2

Royal Bank Group
http://www.rbcroyalbank.com/sme/
http://www.rbcroyalbank.com/agriculture/
http://www.rbcroyalbank.com/agriculture/agadvisor/
http://www.rbcroyalbank.com/sme/index.html
http://www.royalbank.com/agriculture/reviews/

TD Canada Trust Financial Group
http://www.td.com/hr/AAM.jsp

Scotia Bank
http://www.scotiabank.com

BMO Financial Group
http://www4.bmo.com

CIBC Agricultural Services
http://www.cibc.com/ca/small-business/agriculture-serv.html

Business Development Bank
http://www.bdc.ca

5.3 Government business plan advisors

There is a network of regional business centres, advisors and websites in each province/state and territory that can assist you in developing a business plan. There are also both federal and provincial/state agencies in most regions to assist in the process of business planning.

Canadian Business Service Centres/ Government of Canada

The Interactive Business Planner (the IBP) is a computer software program that uses the capabilities of the Internet to assist you in preparing a 3 year business plan for a new or existing business.
http://www.cbsc.org/ibp/doc/intro_ibp.cfm
There are numerous government programs available to assist in the development of a business plan. Some are available through the federal government and many provinces have provincial programs as well.

Agriculture & AgriFood Canada

Canadian Farm Business Advisory Services & Specialized Business Planning Services. **http://www.agr.gc.ca/ren/cfbas/serv_e.cfm**

5.4 Glossary of business plan terminology

Accounts Payable – Amounts owing to suppliers for goods or services received.

Accounts Receivable – Amounts owing from customers for goods or services sold.

Accrual Accounting Method – This method reports revenues when earned not necessarily when they were received. Expenses are reported when incurred not necessarily when they were paid.

Assets – This term includes all items of value owned by the business. (E.g.: Cash, accounts receivable, inventory, equipment, buildings, land and investments.)

Assets (Current) - Current assets are items which can be converted into cash and /or will be used within a short timeframe, normally within one year. (E.g.: Cash, accounts receivable, inventory.)

Assets (Fixed) – Long-term investments in the production of goods or services. These assets are used for more than one year. (E.g.: Equipment, buildings and land.)

Intangible Assets – Other assets that hold value for a business. (E.g.: Trademarks, good will, agreements and rights.)

Liquid Assets – Assets such as cash and short term-investments that can be readily converting into cash with disrupting normal operations.

Balance Sheet - A balance sheet is a statement of a business' financial position, a snapshot in time, showing assets, liabilities, and equity at a particular date.

Capital – The total assets available to a business.

Capital Assets (Long-term Assets) – Assets that have a useful life beyond one year. (E.g.: Land, buildings, equipment and quota.)

Capital Cost Allowance (CCA) – This is the tax term for depreciation which Canada Revenue Agency allows as a deduction for specific business assets.

Capital Gain - Capital gain is the difference between the proceeds from the sale of capital property or asset and its original cost.

Capital Grant – Government grants intended to assist in the purchase of new facilities or equipment.

Cash Flow Statement – A cash flow shows projected sources of cash from business operations, sales, borrowings and owner contributions. It shows anticipated cash payments, business expenses, loan payments, capital purchases and owners withdrawals.

Cash Accounting Method – This method reports income when received and expenses when actually paid.

Change in Inventory – Defines the increase or decrease in the total value of inventory from one reporting period to the next.

Contribution Margin – Is calculated by subtracting the variable expenses from the total revenues.

Cost (Fixed) – Costs that remain unchanged regardless of the volume of production. (E.g.: building insurance, property taxes.)

Cost (Variable) – Costs that vary directly with the volume of production. If no production occurs then there is no variable cost. (E.g.: fertilizer, fuel.)

Cost of Goods Sold – The cost of the products required for the production of goods sold during the business year.

Debt (Current) – A debt or portion of debt that is due within a current year or normal business operating cycle.

Debt (Long - term) – A debt with a maturity beyond one year or beyond a normal business operating cycle.

Debt Capital – Normally the total long-term debt provided to the business by lenders.

Depreciation – A method used to allocate the cost of an asset over its expected life or usefulness. (E.g.: An asset worth $10,000 may be depreciated of 5 years at a rate of 20% per year.)

Dividends – A portion of retained earning as declare by the board of directors of a corporation distributed to shareholders in relation to their shareholdings.

Expenses – A cost associated with the operation of a business during a normal business cycle.

Fair Market Value – The highest dollar value that can be received from the sale of an asset if sold to an unrelated party in an open and unencumbered market.

Fiscal Year - The one year time period for which financial statements are normally prepared.

Gross Margin – Is calculated by subtracting the cost of goods sold from the total revenues representing amounts available for to cover owner and shareholder equity.

Inventory – Tangible items of property which are held for sale or are consumed in the ordinary production operations of a business.

Liabilities – Are obligations or debts owed by a business from past transactions that are to be repaid in the future. (E.g.: Mortgages, loans, accounts payable.) Liabilities are a reduction in a business's equity.

Liabilities (Current) – Bills or amounts owing which are due within a short time frame, the normal operating cycle, one year. (E.g.: Accounts payable and bank operating loans.)

Liabilities (Long-term) – Amounts owing which are due beyond one year or the normal operating cycle. (E.g.: Mortgages and equipment loans.)

Loans (Demand) – A debt for which repayment could be called at any time as per terms of a lenders contract.

Loans (Operating) – Short term loans to a business to cover the normal costs of operation. The loan is normally repayable within one year.

Net Book Value – The value of an asset that is calculated by subtracting the accumulated depreciation from the cost of the asset.

Net Worth Statement – Is a statement summarizing the net worth of an individual at a particular point in time by subtracting liabilities from assets estimated at fair market value.

Note Payable – A liability in the form of a formal written promissory note by a borrower promising to repay a certain amount at a certain time.

Note Receivable – An asset in the form of a written promissory for repayment of a certain amount at a certain time.

Prepaid Expenses – Amounts paid for goods or services to be used in the future. (E.g.: Insurance, property tax, lease deposits.)

Shares – Certificates which represent a person's portion of ownership in a company, often called share capital or capital stock.

Shareholder – The owners of shares in a corporation.

Shareholder's Equity (Owner's Equity) -The excess of the net book value of the assets of an incorporated company that is represented by the shares in that corporation.

Statement of Income and Expenses – Is a financial statement that summarizes the revenue and expenses for a defined business period, a normal operating cycle or a fiscal year of a business.

Statement of Change in Financial Position – Is a statement showing the flow of cash into and out of a business, usually broken down by operating, financing and investment activities over a fiscal period.

Solvency – The ability of a business to pay its long-term debts and obligations.

Working Capital – A business's current assets (cash, accounts receivable, inventory) less its short term debts (accounts payable, operating loans). The difference represents assets available to fund day to day business activities and operations.

5.5 CD-Rom, templates, business plan examples

- Planning templates
- Sample business plans